Praise for Gabriel Fitzmaurice

"the Irish A.A. Milne"

Declan Kiberd, *The Sunday Tribune*

"Ireland's favourite poet for children"

Claire Ranson, *Best Books*

On *The Moving Stair* (Poolbeg 1993):
'*The Moving Stair* includes poems for the very young,
which use the simplest and most ordinary subject
matter, lifted into the realm of the unusual and even
the brilliant by their convincing insights into the
minds of small children . . . Fitzmaurice is the
children's poet who . . . strikes a true chord in the
childlike heart'

Eilís Ní Dhuibhne, *The Lion & the Unicorn, U.S.A.*

On *But Dad!* (Poolbeg 1995):
'*But Dad!* continues in his characteristic vein of
energetic and humorous writing. The poems are written
from the child's viewpoint. They are immediate, short
and play extravagantly with words . . . In the middle of
all this . . . there is some verse which . . . reveals
interesting perceptions of the manner in which children
can experience the world and their place in it'

Tom Mullins, *The Big Guide to Irish Children's Books*

Klaudija

On Puppy and the Sausage (Poolbeg 1998)

'*Puppy and the Sausage* is full of real spontaneous fun'

Ted Hughes

'Classic poems for children'.

Claire Ranson *Children's Books in Ireland*

'*Puppy and the Sausage* is a great collection of poems that will entertain children and adults alike . . . Fitzmaurice has an uncanny empathy with the way kids think and this is brilliantly reflected in every single poem in the book'

Irish Farmers' Monthly

'Hide this collection from your parents because they are bound to want to snaffle it for themselves'

North West Evening Mail, U.K.

'Most of the rhymes reveal the innards of everyday families with a quirky sense of humour. But some have a more serious slant . . . Gabriel [Fitzmaurice] writes simply but tellingly about the ordinary and the everyday and brings them tellingly to life'

Burton Daily Mail, UK

'great fun rhymes'

Northern Echo, U.K.

Dear Grandad
Gabriel Fitzmaurice

Illustrations by
Caroline Hyland

POOLBEG
FOR CHILDREN

Published by
Poolbeg Press Ltd
123 Baldoyle Industrial Estate
Dublin 13, Ireland
E-mail: poolbeg@poolbeg.com
www.poolbeg.com

1 3 5 7 9 10 8 6 4 2

A catalogue record for this book is available from the British Library.

ISBN 1 84223 011 5

Cover design by
Steven Hope

Illustration by
Caroline Hyland

Typeset by
Patricia Hope

Printed by
The Guernsey Press Ltd,
Vale, Guernsey, Channel Islands.

Biography

Gabriel Fitzmaurice was born, in 1952, in Moyvane, Co. Kerry where he still lives. He teaches in the local National School. A former Chair and Literary Advisor of Writers' Week, the Writers' Conference in Listowel, Co. Kerry, he is author of more than twenty books, including poetry in English and Irish, children's verse in English and Irish, translations from the Irish, essays, and collections of songs and ballads. An award winner at the Gerard Manley Hopkins Centenary Poetry Competition, he has twice represented Ireland at the European Festival of Poetry in Louvain, Belgium. A musician and singer, he has played and sung on a number of albums of Irish traditional music. He frequently broadcasts on RTE radio and television and local radio stations on education and the arts.

In memory of the best Grandad in the world,
Jack Fitzmaurice,
with love from John, Nessa,
Mammy and Daddy

Contents

Our New Computer

I love our new computer,
The coolest you can get –
It plays CDs and ROMs and games;
It has the Internet.

I don't know how I did without it –
I could spend all day
In front of our computer
And not go out to play.

It's everything I wanted,
But it can't cuddle me
Or tuck me into bed at night.
It's all I thought 'twould be

But still it's not like people
Or even like my pet –
They really need me.
Our computer doesn't – yet!

Bedtime

A story is cosy
When you go to bed –
It tucks you in and makes you
Cuddly in your head;

Not like a video –
A video's not *read*,
But a story is friendly
And stops you being afraid.

Dad, read me a story
Or I won't go to bed!

Did You Ever?

Did you ever keep your hands in snow
Till it felt that they were hot?
Till they were red and blue like flames
Yet you knew that they were not?

Did you ever snuggle up at night
While the wind wailed overhead?
And the more it wailed, the more you felt
Warm and safe in bed?

Things that are their opposites
That I know with my hands –
Another kind of knowing.
No need to understand.

Hiccups

I like hiccups,
Your stomach jumpin' up
Until it's almost in your mouth –
It's like it is a pup

Bouncin' 'round inside you
But havin' so much fun
He never goes beyond your mouth
Then scampers down again.

And he keeps on playin'
Till, at last too tired to leap,
He settles down inside me,
My puppy fast asleep.

My Rainbow

for Anna McGuire

I made a rainbow of my crayons:
I took them from their pack –
There were greens and reds and yellows
And I threw out the black.

For green's the colour of the grass
And blue is of the sky,
Yellow is the warm round sun
But black is when you cry.

Yellow is a daffodil
And blue is for the sea,
Green is all things growing
And black is not for me.

I gathered up a rainbow,
The promise of the rain –
Though clouds are black and sky is grey,
The sun will shine again.

My New Blue Knickers

I got new blue knickers
In a packet on a hook;
I'm wearing my new knickers –
Do you want to see them? *LOOK!*

I love my new blue knickers,
I'm proud as proud can be –
I can't wait to show my knickers.
EVERYBODY LOOK AT ME!

I got new blue knickers,
I'm proud as proud can be –
I'm ready, are you looking?
MY NEW BLUE KNICKERS – SEE!

Daddy is a Doofus

Daddy is a doofus,
A doofus, a doofus;
Daddy is a doofus,
A doofus because

Daddy is a doofus,
A doofus, a doofus;
Daddy is a doofus
Cos baby said he was.

Combs his hair with fingers,
With fingers, with fingers;
Combs his hair with fingers
With fingers because

Daddy is a doofus,
A doofus, a doofus;
Daddy is a doofus
Cos baby said he was.

Kisses me and misses me,
Misses me, misses me;
Kisses me and misses me,
Misses me because

Daddy is a doofus,
A doofus, a doofus;
Daddy is a doofus
Cos baby said he was.

Sings his songs for sixpence,
For sixpence, for sixpence,
Sings his songs for sixpence,
For sixpence because

Daddy is a doofus,
A doofus, a doofus;
Daddy is a doofus
Cos baby said he was.

Plays with all the children,
The children, the children;
Plays with all the children,
The children because

Daddy is a doofus,
A doofus, a doofus;
Daddy is a doofus
Cos baby said he was.

His belly's like a burger,
A burger, a burger;
His belly's like a burger,
A burger because

Daddy is a doofus,
A doofus, a doofus;
Daddy is a doofus
Cos baby said he was.

Still I love my Daddy,
My Daddy, my Daddy;
Still I love my Daddy,
My Daddy because

Daddy is a doofus,
A doofus, a doofus;
Daddy is a doofus
Cos baby said he was.

Now We Are Eight

Dad, they called you "Gabriel";
Dad, I wonder why –
"Gabriel" 's such a big name
For such a little boy.

Did they always call you "Gabriel",
Dad, when you were small?
Or did your name get bigger
As you grew up? Do all

Our names get bigger, Dad,
When we grow up? You see
I'm not too sure when I grow up
That "Nessa" will fit me.

Dinner

I'm sick of fancy cooking!
Mammy, you're a pro
But *please* for dinner give me
Something that I know

Like chops and spuds and vegebells,
Stuff that I can eat,
And after dinner, Mammy,
Just ice-cream for a treat.

Someday, Mam, I'll eat Chinese,
Italian as well
And you won't have to force me
And I won't have to smell

To see if I can eat it
Mammy when I grow,
But *please* this evening give me
A dinner that I know.

I'm Glad He's my Brother

Though he pushes me and bumps me
And spits at me and thumps me
My brother

And hits me and kicks me
And pulls my hair and flicks me
My brother.

And Daddy says I harry him,
But I won't have to marry him –

That's why I'm glad he's my brother.

The Land of Counterpane

When I am sick and in my bed
I play these games inside my head,
But very soon I'm bored, you see,
Then I get up and watch TV.

Oh! yes I know, in days of old
When children did what they were told,
They stayed in bed all through the day
And made up games that they could play.

But don't you think that, now and then,
They'd turn back the counterpane
And tiptoe down to the settee
And flick through channels just like me
If, long ago, they had TV.

Summer Holidays

Every summer Daddy says
"Where'll we go on holidays?"
And I don't answer cos I know
Just exactly where we'll go –
To the back of some beyond
Where you never hear a sound.
Sure there's mountains, *sure* there's sea –
Big deal! What good is that to me?
I want children who will play
And come to visit every day.
But no! We set off in the car
To anyplace – just so it's far
From everything I like to do
And then I'm told "It's good for you;
Fill your lungs with that fresh air".
My lungs how are you! I don't care –
They can keep their privacy,
Their bogs and mountains, sand and sea –
Every summer, oh my grief!
I wish I was in Tenerife!

Moan

When things are going against me
I could sit down and moan,
But that would get me nowhere –
You always moan alone.

Still, I moan on anyway
Until I reach the end
Of misery and moaning;
At last, my mind's my friend.

And then I stop and wonder
What changed from sad to glee?
And I begin to understand
That nothing changed but me.

Anything But Praise

I don't know how to take a compliment –
When anyone praises me
I panic, make excuses
Smiling squirmingly;

And words race faster than I can think
Giddy as a goat –
Like "The ship must be kept on the road," I blurt,
Or "The show must be kept afloat."

Oh criticize me all you will,
Your sticks and stones won't faze
Cos I can take your worst. Ah yes!
Anything but praise.

Sunday Afternoon
in the Westbury Hotel

We stopped for tea in the Westbury,
We'd been walking half the day
'Round Stephen's Green and Grafton Street
To pass the time away.

My Auntie said, "Let's go for tea,
Let's rest our legs awhile",
So we went for tea in the Westbury.
Oh my, that place has style!

'Twas bigger than a football field
And lush as luxury;
The place was full of millionaires –
'Twas fifteen quid for tea.

As I was finishing my *Coke,*
My Daddy said, "Look, John!
D'you see that man who's just come in?
That man's a Rolling Stone".

I thought that he was joking
As only Daddy could,
But he said "I'm not fooling –
That's Ronnie Wood".

He sat there on a sofa
In a black suit, all alone –
He didn't look like the photos
Of the rockin' Rolling Stones.

I asked Dad to get his autograph
But I think he was too shy
So I went over to Ronnie Wood –
"Mister Wood", says I,

"Would you please give me your autograph,
We have the Stones' CDs".
Ronnie Wood looked up at me
(I think that he was pleased).

He asked my name, where I came from,
And I was thinking "Wow!
What would my friends down in Moyvane
Think of me now?"

"My autograph's worth nothing",
Whispered Ronnie Wood;
Then he took out two pounds and smiled
"Have this from me instead".

Two pounds! But I won't spend it;
I'll keep it safe at home –
Two silver discs, just think of it
That I got from a Rolling Stone.

Buying a Dictionary

I went to buy a dictionary –
They all looked grand and thick,
So I decided to check them out:
I looked up "Neolithic"

In this Mini *Oxford*
And there it was, so I
Bought the *Mini Oxford* –
'Twas as good as I could buy.

When I showed it to my Daddy,
At first he looked quite pleased
That I had bought an *Oxford* –
But he had to screw his eyes

The print there was so tiny;
I thought then that he'd scold,
And so to head him off I said
"Dad, you're getting old –

Your eyes are not what they used to be
When you, too, were a child";
My Daddy closed the dictionary
And smiled –

"That's the way, son", Daddy said,
"I suppose I'm getting old;
My eyes are not what they used to be".
And I wish I'd let him scold.

21

My Best Friend

My best friend was Grandad.
I used to stay at his house on Friday nights
And that was great fun.
He used to take me to the chipper
After the nine o'clock news
And he'd buy two cartons of curried chips
and two sausages
And we'd eat them in his kitchen during
the *Late Late Show.*
He used to come up to our house on
Sundays for dinner
And I'd always want to sit beside him at the table.

I remember one Christmas I had just got
a snooker table.
Grandad came up for Christmas dinner
And I had asked everybody else to play with me.
They all said no, they were too busy.
Grandad was in the middle of setting the table
And I asked him to play and he said he would.
He came over
And I actually had to place the balls for him
It was so long since he had played snooker!

Well Grandad was my best friend;
He was so kind.
He was just unique to me.
Like he didn't know much Irish
Because when he was young he hadn't
much time for school
(He had to help at home on the farm, he said,
And at fourteen had to hire himself with farmers
Because he had thirteen brothers and sisters
And times were bad)
But I often did my Irish homework with him
and he always ended up right.

I remember the day Grandad died.
It was March.
I can't remember the date.
He rang Mom and said he thought he was
    having a heart attack.
We rushed down to his house –
We got there in two and a half minutes
And when we went in we found
    Grandad lying on the floor moaning.
And then he just died.
And I was below in the room crying
And then Mom and Nessa and Dad started
    crying too.

At the Funeral Parlour I forgot myself
And said "I'm sitting beside Grandad".
But Grandad was in his coffin.

He was dead.

It was fine until they closed the coffin
And then I knew I'd never see him
again in this life.

Goodbye, Grandad, my best friend.
Goodbye
Goodbye.

adapted from a story written by my son John

Dear Grandad

Dear Grandad,
I hope you are happy
Because we are very sad.
I wish you were here
Because I miss you so much.

At first I was angry
When you died.
I cried and cried.

I love you, Grandad;
I miss you.

Nessa says that God took you
To mind his garden in Heaven,
To make new flowers grow
Like you do in your garden.

I don't know.

Well, Grandad,
It's time to face reality.
I'll plant flowers on your grave;
I know you'll like that.
Mammy and Daddy say they'll let me.

Grandad,
I hope you enjoy your immortality.
Twice today I saw you smile at me.
Goodnight, Grandad,
I miss you, miss you, miss you.
John.

A Poem for Grandad

I made a poem for Grandad;
Most of it is true
Except for bits and pieces.
Things we used to do,

The fun we had together –
I told it like it was,
The truth of me and Grandad;
I made up bits because

Grandad's now my story –
I imagine him to be
The things we did together
And little bits of me.

I made a poem for Grandad;
Grandad's five weeks dead –
Now Grandad is the story
I see inside my head.

Hallowe'en

It's Hallowe'en! We dead are seen!
Tonight's our night to act up mean;
Now mere mortals are afraid –
It's great to be dead!

We haunt them from beyond the grave;
Tonight we rollick revel rave;
Now mere mortals are afraid –
It's great to be dead!

For dead we are but not tonight,
Petty mortals walk in light:
Oh tonight they're all afraid –
It's great to be dead!

And the mortals pray pray pray
That the dead will keep away,
But they'll die too one by one
And they'll join us in the fun.

It's Hallowe'en! Rise up! Be seen!
Hear the children laugh and scream
All masked up and not afraid
Pretending to be dead.

The Bloodstain on the Floor

The devil came at midnight
When the village was asleep
Except for one lone student
Who was in study deep
And at the stroke of midnight
His flesh began to creep.

The devil came at midnight
As fear began to float,
He came at the stroke of midnight
And turned into a stoat;
The stoat attacked the student
And ripped his milk-white throat.

The red, red blood began to flow
On the wooden floor,
The student fell as pale as death
Covered in his gore
And at the stroke of one o'clock
The student breathed no more.

And the blood stayed in the timber
Scrub it as they might
And screams were heard from the empty room
In the dead of night;
They put a new floor on the old
To keep the blood from sight.

But the blood showed through the timber –
It's there for all to see:
A hundred years and still it's there,
And there it's going to be –
The devil's sign upon the floor
For all eternity.

A Walk in the Country

It's hard to find a toilet
When you're bursting for the loo
And you're somewhere in the country –
What are you to do?

You try to find a quiet spot
Behind a tree or ditch
But *ouch!* - Ah yes, a nettle
Stings you and you itch.

And if, in desperation,
You sneak into a wood,
A crow is doing his business
And it lands upon your head.

Or if in haste you disappear
Down a shady lane,
Alas! the road less travelled
Ends up in a drain;

And your socks and shoes are squelchy
And you wish you hadn't come
For a walk out in the country;
You turn around for home

Cos it's hard to find a toilet
When you're bursting for the loo
And the countryside is treacherous
When you haven't got a clue.

"It's the Times"

I saw a photo of when Dad was young
Working on the farm,
But there was something wrong with it –
The cows had tails and horns.

Now everybody knows that's wrong –
Who ever saw a cow
With tail and horns, I ask you?
But I started thinking how

Useful a tail would be
To flick away the flies,
Though horns could be dangerous –
They could gouge out your eyes.

So then I asked my Daddy
(He's no longer on the farm –
He married in the city)
How come the cows had horns

And great big tails when he was young
And then my Daddy smiled:
"That's the way they're meant to be.
When I was a child

All the cows had horns and tails –
It's the way they're born,
But nature must be enhanced
If you want to run a farm –

You've got to make a profit
Even if that means
Tampering with nature
So all the beef is lean

And all the cows milk gallons,
It's the practice, it's the times.
Farming is a business –
That's the bottom line.

The old ways are outdated",
My Daddy said to me;
"But Dad", I said, "In the old days
There was no BSE".

You mess about with nature,
I think, at your peril".
Daddy smiled, a slow sad smile:
"It's the times, my girl".

The Birds are Growing
on the Trees

The birds are growing on the trees,
And roses bloom anew as bees,
The hedge is plastered nest by nest –
This is the way I see things best:

Things I see that aren't quite
Yet saying somehow makes them right;
Things that live by being said –
Otherwise they're simply dead.

The Beggar

Brings his blessings
Even to those who refuse his
Grace.
Go and feed
All nations, the whole human
Race.

The Teacher

Talks about
Education
And how
Children should
Have their say
Even though he always
Runs things his own way.

April Fool

I forgot today was "April Fool"
And I was sitting here in school
When the teacher asked for a volunteer
To go to the Garage to get him
A number seven button for a mobile phone.

I volunteered
And off I ran
To Dennis's Garage in Moyvane
For a number seven button for a mobile phone.

When I asked Dennis, he just smiled –
He knew the score and laughed,
"Poor child!
Tell your teacher I have no
Number seven button for a mobile phone".

So I walked back all alone
Cursing that mobile phone
And the teacher
And the school
And that silly "April Fool"
And myself that volunteered.

When I came in
My classmates cheered
"April Fool, boy!
April Fool!"

Sometimes life can be so cruel.

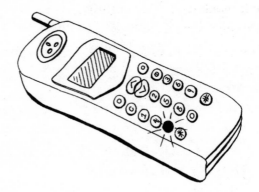

Grammar

Ebenezer Egghead
Is such a clever fellow,
He *loves* to show off all he knows
So much he needs to tell you.

He boasts about his grammar
But once I caught him right:
I asked him which was more correct –
"The yolk of an egg *is* white"
Or "The yolk of an egg *are* white".

He looked at me disdainfully,
He's such a clever fellow:
"The yolk of an egg *is* white", he snapped.
(The yolk of an egg *is* yellow!)

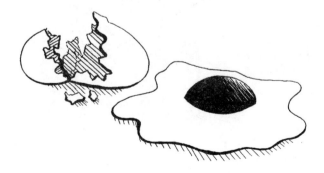

What's a Tourist?

"Children, what's a tourist?
Can anyone tell me now?"

"Please sir, a man with a camera
Taking photos of a cow!"

Dreaming Chuck Berry

I was asked to write a story
Of doing my favourite things –
The only thing I want to do
Is play upon my strings,

My red and white cutaway
Rock 'n' roll guitar
Dreaming that I'm up on stage
Chuck Berry, a rock star.

I strum to all his singles
My Daddy has on tape –
He's given me the loan of it
And boy! Chuck Berry's great.

I know all the lyrics
"Johnny B. Goode" and all –
Some day, like him, I'll be in lights
Over every concert hall.

But I can't write what I want to
Cos my spelling's below par;
I'll write *I play the banjo* –
It's easier than *guitar.*

So it's *banjo* for the teacher
Cos I can spell it right,
Guitar for the rock star
Whose name's up there in lights.

Learning the Tin Whistle

I'm learning the tin whistle –
I play it really fast,
But the tune just runs away from me
(In this race, I'm always last).

The more the tune runs onwards,
The faster I must play
Till I run out of fingers
And the tune gets clean away.

Come back *Peg Ryan's Polka*,
The Dawning of the Day,
The Britches Full of Stitches,
Come back and let me play.

I'll play you soft and easy,
I'll practise day and night –
Oh please slow down and wait for me
Till the music comes out right.

I'll play you soft and easy
Till feet tap on the ground
And all the air is music
In my cylinder of sound.

Come back *Peg Ryan's Polka,*
Give me one more chance –
My notes will turn to music
When my fingers learn to dance.

Tractors

for Denic Mac

Every time I draw a picture
I put a tractor in –
Like a Lamborghini
Or a Massey Ferguson.

When I drew Cinderella
Going to the ball,
I put her in a Zetor
Slippers, gown and all.

And when the teacher asked us
To draw a motor race,
I drew Michael Schumacher
And put him in a Case.

And when I drew the Pope
On his visit to Mexico,
Did I put him in the Popemobile?
Indeed I didn't. No!

I put him in a trailer –
A great big massive Kane,
The kind you use for silage
And not so much for praying.

And when I had to draw
A parable of the Lord,
I drew the one of sowing seeds
And put him in a Ford.

And when the King of Jordan died,
Did I put him in a hearse?
No way! I drew the funeral
With the coffin in an Ursus.

Oh Lord! I just love tractors!
And all I want to be
Is a hundred horsepower jockey
When I'm grown up and free.

A Child Visits the Musée Picasso

This fellow's really funny –
He's welded some guitars;
There's a bull's head: it's a bicycle –
The saddle and handlebars!

And ladies with funny noses,
A Pierrot like I'd seen
(In the Louvre, by Watteau, Dad said) –
He looks like Mr. Bean.

There were statues there with willies
Pointing straight at me,
And statues more like robots,
And a squiggly family.

I think I could draw better
Now that I am eight;
But Picasso's really funny.
I think Picasso's great!

Picasso

I called him Pablo Pissasso,
The 'c' as in Celtic, you know;
In Glasgow they all call it "Seltic".
I support Glasgow Celtic. And so

I called him Pablo *Pissasso*
Reading the way I've been taught
Breaking down words into phonics
But look at the word that I got!

Pablo *Pissasso* I called him
Now I'll never forget the guy's name –
Pickasso, Pickasso, Pickasso
The sound of the Spanish, my shame.

Pissasso I read for the teacher
But she only turned and smiled.
"Pick-asso", she told me; "Look, children!
The man who could paint like a child".

Alfresco

Self portraits – Rembrandt and Picasso;
The class looks on; the masters are revered –
They prefer Rembrandt to Picasso,
But number one's Van Gogh – "the orange beard".

A week later, the sun is shining;
Experience knows how pupils must be steered –
The teacher says "We're going to draw *alfresco*".
"Is he the lad", one asks, "with the orange beard?"

Hollywood

There's nice boys out in Hollywood,
I saw them on TV,
With the whitest smiles and brownest tans –
That's where I'd like to be

Where all the boys are film stars
Not like the lads 'round here
Whose skin is white, whose teeth are brown,
Who dress in awful gear.

There's nice boys out in Hollywood –
That's where I'd like to be
Instead of being stuck at home
In dull reality.

Miss Romance

Miss Romance writes the names
Of all the boys in class
And underneath, the girls' names,
Between them draws pink hearts –

So Jennifer loves Andrew
And Josephine loves Paul
And Bernadette loves Billy;
Miss Romance pairs them all

No matter that Bernadette
Can't stand Billy's looks
And Jennifer hates Andrew
And Josie'd rather books;

At twelve, she pairs them anyway –
She knows things that you know
When the boys you sit beside in class
No longer are the foe.

Love

Billy Kirkpatrick in Fifth Class
Is such a cute little chap –
I'd like it if he was my boyfriend:
I'll give him a wear of my cap.

I wonder if Billy will wear it –
If he does, I know what it means
(It means that he really likes me –
A boyfriend! Just like in my dreams!)

He's taken my cap and it fits him
Just, you might say, like a glove –
I hope that he'll keep it forever.
Oh boy! but this surely is love.

The Part of Mary in the Christmas Play

I got the part of Mary
In the Christmas play –
'Twas grand until I realized
I had no lines to say.

First the Angel came to me –
I had to bow my head
And look as sickly sweet as pie.
I wish I'd lines instead.

Then I had to follow Joseph –
I had no lines to say
(Even the two dressed as the donkey
Got to bray);

But I had to follow Joseph
Quiet as a mouse
While he went from inn to inn
And house to boarding house.

Then I had to hold the baby
When the shepherds came to pray;
And the same again for the Wise Men.
I wish I'd lines to say.

Don't you think that Mary
Would get to say a word;
After all, 'twas *she* that chose –
The mother of the Lord!

Don't you think that such a woman
Would have more to do
Than look as sickly sweet as pie
Forever dressed in blue?

Don't you think that such a woman
Should have lines to say
Instead of being an extra
In the Christmas play?

Paddy Last

My friends all call me "Paddy Last" –
I am an also ran,
Behind at everything I do
Since my life began.

At lessons I'm just useless;
At music I can't sing;
For work – well, I'm too clumsy;
I can't do anything.

But Sunday in the village sports
I entered for the sprint;
I'd never run a race before –
I entered this event

Because it was the shortest
And all I had to do
Was run a hundred metres
Without sock or shoe.

I started at the whistle
And sizzled to the line
And I was first to breast the tape,
The others 'way behind.

"And the medal goes to Paddy Last"
I could hear the village roar.
"Now I'm first at last", I cried,
"I was always behind before".

Running Away

He's running away from his Mammy,
He's running away from his Dad –
He can't take any more so he's leaving;
He's snivelling, he's snuffling, he's mad.

So he goes to his room in a fury
(Making sure that his Daddy can see)
And fills up his bag with his Teddies.
But Dad just sits, cool as can be.

And he slams the front door so they'll hear him
And he sobs as he walks down the drive
And he keeps looking back towards the window
To see if the curtains are moved.

Slowly he walks down the driveway –
Oh Daddy, please call me back,
Oh Mammy, come quickly and save me,
I'm sorry now that I packed.

And he stops at the gate and he wonders
Just where do I think I am going?
And Daddy comes out and he hugs him –
It's good not to feel so alone.

"Son, where did you think you were going?
We love you, we need you, you know".
"Oh Daddy, sure I was just bluffing.
Thanks for not letting me go".

In the Attic

You're going up in the attic, Dad –
Please can I come too?
I'll even get the ladder, Dad,
And put it up for you.

Of all the places in our house
I love the attic best;
It's dark there – dark as Christmas
With every box a chest

Of surprise and promise –
The things we store up there
Are put away like memories
To open if you dare.

You're going up in the attic, Dad –
Can I come up too, *please!*
For hidden in the attic
Among the memories

Is part of me and part of you –
The part we seldom show;
Oh, up there in the attic, Dad,
Is all we're not, below.

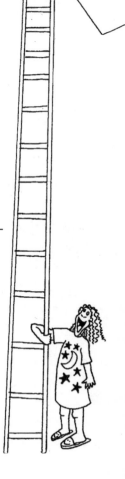

Old Tom

Just an old man leaning
On the schoolyard wall,
He spends his mornings dreaming –
Yes! He's known them all,

The children of the parish
(He's loved them as his own);
Still, he sees them playing,
Those boys and girls long grown.

He sees them and he smiles at them
As he recites their names
For all his joy is watching
Children at their games.

He pictures what an open eye
Cannot see at all,
This old man dreaming
On the schoolyard wall.

Snowy
The Puppy the Circus Left Behind

Snowy is the puppy
The circus left behind,
A little mongrel puppy.
The circus was unkind

To leave behind the puppy
Lonely and alone;
He hung around the village
Looking for a home.

The circus dogs were beautiful
Groomed for the magic lights,
But little puppy Snowy
Was tied up day and night

For he was but a mongrel,
Not beautiful or proud;
The circus kept him hidden
From the crowd

Tied up behind a caravan
All day hungry, sad
And no-one listened to him.
He wished that he was dead.

His mother in the circus
Wasn't allowed to see
Her little puppy Snowy –
Mammy had to be

With the other circus dogs
Performing every day;
She longed to see her Snowy
But the pup was kept away.

And so the circus moved on
But left the pup behind;
He wandered through the village
Hoping he could find

A shed, a barn to lay down
But there was no room for him;
He slept outside the carpenter's
And the carpenter took him in.

He put him in the workshop
That night, and then next day
Snowy roamed the village
Looking for someone to play

With him and be his friend
And pat him on the head;
When the village children found him
They brought him milk and bread.

And he'd play with them and lick them
All the summer long
But one day in September
His friends were gone.

Where were all the children,
His friends, his playmates gone?
Nowhere in the village –
Again he was alone.

He wandered round the village
Empty as the street
Searching for the children
On little lonely feet.

He sat down at the Corner
Where dust and papers lay
Before the breezes played with them
And carried them away.

And who would play with Snowy
And carry him away
To the magic that he came from
Today or any day?

He sat down at the Corner
Head between his paws,
Nothing else to do now
But snooze.

And he snoozed there at the Corner
And he began to dream
That he was with the children
Till wakened by their screams –

The children! Yes, the children!
He heard them, plain as day
(The children in the school yard
At play).

What's this? What's this? The children
Playing beyond that wall!
He scampered to the school yard;
He could hear the children call

"Snowy, Snowy, Snowy,
Come here and join our play",
But the teachers saw the mongrel
And shooed him away.

Snowy left the school yard
With all his friends at play;
He sat in the roadway watching
And slowly slunk away.

But when their play was over
And the kids were back in school,
Snowy slipped into the yard
(Oh! Snowy was no fool!);

He gobbled the ends of sandwiches
The children couldn't eat;
He chased the crows around the yard
And peed against the gate;

He sat down in the school yard
And stretched out in the sun;
At three o'clock the bell rang
And his friends were out again.

And day by day he came to school
When the kids were in their class
And he'd sit there in the school yard
And watch the traffic pass

Till one day he grew bolder
And came at lunch time when
The children were out playing.
He was shooed away again

By the teachers who were worried
That the dog might bite
And frighten the small children.
Snowy jumped the gate

But when the teachers turned away
He jumped the gate again
And came back to the children
Who cheered and clapped their friend.

The teachers turned a blind eye
To Snowy after that
And every day he'd come to school
And sit upon the mat

Just inside the front door
Till the bell would ring for play,
Then he'd scamper with the children
And the teachers kept away.

And though he is no circus dog,
He's up to lots of tricks
Playing football with his friends –
He jumps and catches, flicks

The ball on with his head,
Carries in his mouth;
He's as good as any goalie
But prefers to play out-

Field with the children
And when they've finished play,
Snowy sits and scratches
Or chases the crows away.

Night time in the village,
Stars sparkle overhead,
The village curls up like a dog
Settling in its bed;

Snowy in the workshop
Asleep in golden straw
Dreaming of the children,
Head upon his paw,

Happy in a village
That's so very kind
To a little mongrel puppy
The circus left behind.